Comprehension

Book 3

Liz Ross-Elsden

HOPSCOTCH
EDUCATIONAL PUBLISHING

Published by
Hopscotch Educational Publishing Ltd
Unit 2
The Old Brushworks
56 Pickwick Road
Corsham
Wiltshire
SN13 9BX

01249 701701

© 2004 Hopscotch Educational Publishing

Written by Liz Ross-Elsden
Series design by Blade Communications
Cover illustration by Susan Hutchison
Illustrated by Catherine Ward
Printed by Colorman (Ireland) Ltd

ISBN 1-904307-22-1

Acknowledgements
The authors and publisher gratefully acknowledge permission to
reproduce copyright material in this book.
'Shut your mouth when you're eating' by Michael Rosen,
originally published in *Quick, Let's Get Out of Here*. Copyright ©
Micjhael Rosen, 1983. All rights reserved. First published by Andre
Deutsch and reproduced by kind permission of Scholastic Ltd.

Every effort has been made to trace the owners of copyright of
material in this book and the publisher apologises for any
inadvertent omissions. Any persons claiming copyright for any
material should contact the publisher who will be happy to pay
the permission fees agreed between them and who will amend
the information in this book on any subsequent reprint.

The National Literacy Strategy Framework – Text level links for Year 5

		T1	T2	T3	T4	T5	T6	T7	T8	T9	T10	T11	T12	T13	T14	T15	T16	T17	T18	T19	T20	T21	T22	T23	T24	T25	T26	T27
Term 1	Activity 1	•																										
	Activity 2	•																										
	Activity 3	•																										
	Activity 4			•																								
	Activity 5			•		•																						
	Activity 6				•																							
	Activity 7							•																				
	Activity 8							•																				
	Activity 9								•																			
	Activity 10								•																			
	Activity 11																				•							
	Activity 12																						•					
	Activity 13																						•					
	Activity 14																						•		•			
	Activity 15																							•				
	Activity 16																									•		
	Activity 17																									•		
	Activity 18																									•		
	Activity 19																									•		
	Activity 20																										•	
Term 2	Activity 21	•																										
	Activity 22	•																										
	Activity 23	•																										
	Activity 24				•																							
	Activity 25				•																		•					
	Activity 26						•																					
	Activity 27						•																					
	Activity 28									•																		
	Activity 29										•																	
	Activity 30													•														
	Activity 31															•												
	Activity 32															•												
	Activity 33															•		•										
	Activity 34															•		•										
	Activity 35															•		•			•							
	Activity 36															•		•										
	Activity 37															•		•										
	Activity 38																	•				•						
	Activity 39															•		•				•						
	Activity 40															•						•						
Term 3	Activity 41	•	•																									
	Activity 42			•																								
	Activity 43						•																					
	Activity 44					•				•																		
	Activity 45						•																					
	Activity 46						•																					
	Activity 47						•																					
	Activity 48								•																			
	Activity 49						•																					
	Activity 50									•																		
	Activity 51												•			•	•											
	Activity 52												•			•	•			•								
	Activity 53																•											
	Activity 54																•											
	Activity 55																•											
	Activity 56																•											
	Activity 57																•											
	Activity 58																•											
	Activity 59																		•									
	Activity 60																			•								

Today, more than ever, it is important that children can read and interpret text in many different forms. Traditional narrative is still important but, increasingly, vital information is now presented in a wide range of formats including graphs, flow charts, diagrams, timelines, pictures and illustrations. The overwhelming abundance of information available from internet sources places increasing demands on children to locate, sort, understand and interpret information more quickly than ever before. This series aims to help children develop strategies that will enable them to succeed in our information-overloaded world!

About this series

Comprehension is a series of books aimed at developing key comprehension skills across Key Stage 2 and the first years of Key Stage 3.

The series aims to set the children thinking! It requires them not only to interpret what they read but to use the information they have gathered in a constructive way, by applying it to, for example, graphs, maps, diagrams, pictures and tables. Alternatively, many of the activities require the children to explain in words information that is contained in different visual representations, such as graphs, diagrams and illustrations. The *Comprehension* series aims to stimulate children so that they see things from a different perspective and to respond in a variety of ways.

There are four books in the series. Each book is matched to the National Literacy Strategy's *Framework for Teaching* as set out below, but we are confident that the books are flexible enough to be used across the age ranges from Year 3 to Year 8.

> Book 1 – Year 3
> Book 2 – Year 4
> Book 3 – Year 5
> Book 4 – Year 6

Each book aims to:
- ❑ develop children's inferential skills, encouraging them to 'read between the lines' where they have to search for hidden clues or make a link between cause and effect;
- ❑ develop children's deductive skills, enabling them to relate information in the text to their own experiences and background knowledge;
- ❑ develop children's evaluative skills to encourage critical evaluation and expression of opinion;
- ❑ support teachers by providing a programme that can be matched term by term to the NLS *Framework for Teaching* or can be 'dipped into' as and when required;
- ❑ encourage enjoyment and curiosity as well as develop skills of interpretation and response.

Each book is divided into ten fiction and ten non-fiction activities per term. These are listed on page 3, which also contains a chart that shows the *Framework's* Text level objective/s that each activity addresses.

Many of the activities are cross-curricular, taking in aspects of science, history and geography, for example. Other activities are centred around the interests of children, and topics such as magic, Martians, wizards and dragons are included. All the activities are intended to be fun as well as purposeful!

Using the activities

The activities are versatile enough to be used as part of whole-class lessons, group work or homework /reinforcement tasks. The teacher's role is to introduce the activity, carry out any revision of terms that may be necessary and put the task into a suitable context. Many of the activities would benefit from being discussed in pairs or small groups before commencing.

It is important to stress to the children that they read the complete text (including the required tasks) before they actually do anything. This helps to ensure they understand what they have to do before they begin. Their answers could be formulated in note form before reading through the activity again to make sure there has been no misunderstanding.

Name _____

The dare

Jennifer waded through the long grass and weeds and stood in front of the house. It was like something out of an old black and white movie. It was an ugly grey wooden house with a wide front verandah and four sharp turrets, one at each corner of the house. It certainly *looked* like it was haunted. The room on the far right had been the girl's bedroom. It was the only unbroken window of the four facing the street and standing up at that window was a large and odd-looking doll wearing a tatty, old-fashioned white frock with torn lace frills. Jennifer forced herself to look straight at its one eye. It didn't wink at her. She was so relieved! It still looked spooky though. Why did it have just one eye and hair on only half of its head? Perhaps the house wasn't haunted after all. There were no lights flashing on and off either.

She quickly went up to the huge panelled front door, opened it and took a few steps backwards. The door creaked and groaned. A strong old, musty smell made her gasp and a strange cold feeling enveloped her. So far, so good, she tried to tell herself. She listened carefully... no strange sounds like a ball bouncing, a drum being hit or a wind-up toy clicking and whirring. As she peered in at the hallway a light breeze swept some dust along the floor. She looked up the stairs and saw cobwebs at the corners of the handrail. She talked aloud, "It's just an old house. There's nothing to worry about!" She didn't really believe her own words. She did not want to go in but she had to get the one-eyed doll. She had to show Jaz she wasn't a "feeble, frightened little girlie". This boast had definitely been one of her worst ideas yet though. There must be a better way to prove her point. Jennifer decided not to put it off any longer. Thinking about it made it worse. She quickly ran through the door and up the stairs... CRASH! The front door slammed. Jennifer froze on the stairs too frightened even to scream. Seconds later she became aware of some strange sounds... whirring, clicking and banging.

1. Jennifer didn't want to go to the house. Why exactly was she there?

2. What strange phenomena had people said happened at the house?

3. What evidence is there in the text that the house hadn't been occupied for a long time?

4. Draw the outside of the house with the doll in the window.

Name _____

Wrong time, wrong place

❑ Below is the opening scene from a film. Read it carefully and then draw a storyboard to show the sequence of events as Murali experienced them.

Murali ran for his life back through the warehouse doors and up the alley. He needed to get to the main street. He could lose himself there. He glanced over his shoulder. The rain stung his eyes and the alley was dimly lit but he could see the four men were just 200 yards behind him. "Help me!" he screamed. There was no one to hear. Where was the main street? Right? Keep running. Another backward glance told him one of the men was closing fast – only 100 yards now. Left? Yes. He could see the main street. He shouted to the few people who were walking in the street but they just looked at him like he was crazy. He ran through the nearest open door. It was a theatre. Where now? No time to think. He ran to the cloakroom and jumped over the counter, to the astonishment of the attendant. Murali could hardly talk he was so out of breath.

"They're... going to... kill me," he managed as he wriggled behind some long coats on a rack. The attendant seemed to compose herself as she hurriedly wiped the counter, sat down, and picked up the magazine she had dropped. Murali's heart felt like it was coming out of his chest. His breathing seemed so loud. He fought to slow it down. He realised he was trembling. He tried to control that too!

Minutes passed. This was all so crazy. How had he got himself into this mess? His biggest problem earlier had only been a slight headache. If only he had got a taxi back to the hotel from the club or let one of his friends take him home as they had suggested. He cursed his sense of direction. It had never been good. He had only wanted to ask for directions. What were they doing in there anyway? He had only seen the two men and the suitcases ... and the gun in one man's jacket. This was one holiday he would never forget! Then the chilling thought hit him that he may not live to remember it! It was all so unbelievable and so horribly real!

Name _____

Trust us!

❑ Design a poster that outlines all the points that the boys' mother wants them to remember.

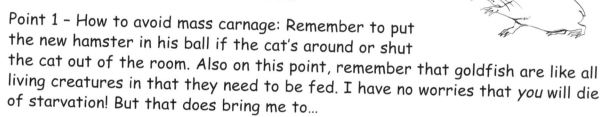

Christine looked at her three boys smiling at her and sighed.

"Now I'm trusting you! Heaven knows why! I know I'm only away for a week and you are all a year older and hopefully wiser but I want to go over the important points again. Are you all listening? What lessons did we learn from the last time we tried this?

Point 1 – How to avoid mass carnage: Remember to put the new hamster in his ball if the cat's around or shut the cat out of the room. Also on this point, remember that goldfish are like all living creatures in that they need to be fed. I have no worries that *you* will die of starvation! But that does bring me to...

Point 2 – Try not to have all three meals each day at the fast food restaurant around the corner! I know he gave you discounts for eating there so often but it really isn't good for you. I've put lots of freshly cooked meals in the freezer. You don't need to cook, just push some buttons on the microwave.

Point 3 – How to avoid the invasion of the flies: Please clean the cat bowl and put fresh food in it daily. I'm sure it was fascinating to watch the maggots squirming around in the old cat food but it wasn't the welcome home I was hoping for.

Point 4 – How to avoid visits from the police: Firstly, while I'm sure you have seen people on telly climbing onto a porch roof and smashing a window to get into a house, it isn't clever when there are copies of the house key with no less than five neighbours. So if you do happen to lock yourself out, please try them all first. Yes, you were unlucky that Mr Glenn didn't recognise you but he was trying to protect the house. Secondly, loud music and hundreds of noisy teenagers until 2am are NOT good ideas! Yes, Mr Glenn could perhaps have talked to you first about his concerns before phoning the police but he was within his rights.

Point 5 – How to hold on to your pocket money! If you damage any household item you will pay for it to be replaced. Yes, I know that none of us liked the framed family photo your Uncle Dave gave us but that's not the point!

Do you understand all that? How I'm supposed to relax on holiday I'll never know!"

Name _____

No way back

The policeman banged on the door.

"This is the police. Open up," he shouted. The sounds of the twins arguing was getting louder.

The policewoman who was with him looked through the letterbox. She saw Darren putting the box in the cupboard under the sink. Then he came to the door and let them in.

The policewoman went straight for the cupboard.

"Well, Darren, we've not seen you for a while. I was just starting to miss you," said the policeman sarcastically.

"I've been behaving myself. Got a *proper* job as well. You should get one," smiled Darren cheekily.

The policewoman took out the box and opened it. Darren and his brother Dave looked at each other. Inside were the car stereos.

"Is this what you call behaving yourself?" asked the policeman. "Are you going to admit it this time? There are no prints I assume? But you'll be surprised to learn we've got you on video. Not too clear but it'll do. Once you started nicking there was no way back for you was there? I knew it was only a matter of time!"

Dave looked like he was about to say something when Darren went over to him. "Shut it. If you say a word I will kill you." Then he went over to the box and with an air of defiance put his hands all over the top stereos. Then he turned and smiled at the policeman and said, "There you go... happy?"

"Right, you're nicked son," said the policeman.

A couple of weeks later Dave went to visit Darren in prison.

"I'm so, so sorry," said Dave. "I don't know why I did it... They kept saying I couldn't do it. That I was nothing like you. It should be me in here!"

"Don't worry about it. That copper was right. There's no way back for me. There is for you. Promise me that was your first and last time," said Darren.

"Yes. I promise, but please don't say there's no way back for you, OK? There is. You hadn't done anything for four months. You'll get another job," Dave pleaded.

Darren smiled weakly.

1. Retell the story in your own words.

2. What does Darren's character seem to be at the beginning of the story? What makes you think that?

3. How does the writer portray Darren's character at the end of the story? What makes you think that?

Name _____

What did he look like?

Scene: A police artist is called to the Abbott's house. One of the twin boys in the family disturbed a burglar the night before.

Police artist (to family): Now, just take your time and describe the person you saw in the lounge last night. Be as detailed as possible.

Mother (trying to cuddle the twins): Oh. It is all just so awful! Awful!

Twin 1 (to Mum): Get off me, Mum. (to police artist) I'll tell you what happened. It's me you need to talk to. I scared him off you know! (puffing himself up proudly).

Twin 2 (laughing): YOU scared HIM? That's a laugh. You ran up the stairs screaming and hid in the bathroom!

Twin 1 (snaps at Twin 2): Shut up! (turns back to police artist) I heard a noise downstairs and went to investigate. (pointing to Twin 2) He wouldn't have heard a thing … he snores like a pig!

Twin 2 (indignant): No I don't!

Mum (fidgeting and biting a fingernail): Boys, boys. Shush now. (to police artist) Sorry. We're just all so shaken!

Police artist: OK. Can we just get to the description of the person please?

Twin 1: Yeah. He wants ME to talk! (coughs, dramatically) It was pitch black as I marched into the lounge, except for the torch that he had put down by the telly. He was bent over near it so I could see his face clearly. He had an evil face.

Police artist: What was his hair like?

Twin 1: He had long, straight hair down to his shoulders.

Police artist: Fringe?

Twin 1: Yes. It was down over his eyes.

Police artist: Was the hair dark or light?

Twin 1: Dark.

Police artist: What kind of face did he have?

Twin 1: Ugly. (pointing to Twin 2) Like his! Really evil! (he laughs)

Twin 2 (snaps): We're identical twins you idiot!

Police artist (impatiently): Which face shape? Was it round?

Twin 1: No. Long and thin. Everything was long and thin. Narrow eyes. Thin lips.

Police Artist: Moustache? Beard?

Twin 1: No.

Police Artist: Anything else? Tattoos, jewellery?

Twin 1 (thinks for a second): Yes. An earring. A cross. In the … right ear.

Police Artist (relieved): Thank you.

1. What can you say about Mum's character?

2. How would you describe the relationship between the twins?

3. Draw an impression of the burglar from the information above.

Name _____

A time of change

It was a crisp, frosty autumn morning. Liz took her daughter Jade for a walk in the woods. She thought the walk might help. She knew Jade wasn't happy. The move had been difficult for her. She was a sensitive girl and shy and she hadn't settled well at her new school. She missed her old school and her old friends.

"Are you warm enough?" asked her mum, taking her hand. Jade kept looking down but nodded.

"It's great having a wood near our new house isn't it?" Liz asked. Jade just kicked some leaves.

"I love walking on days like this. There are so many changes going on," said Liz.

"What changes?" asked Jade.

"The change in fashion for a start." Jade frowned. Her mum continued, "Some wear green all the time. Others are throwing off their summer collection at the moment."

She covered Jade's eyes. "And... Oh don't look, some are completely nude!" Jade tried to hide it but she was smiling.

"Because of these changes we'll see red, yellow and brown butterflies this time of year. Let's see if we can find any. Then there's the jewels. As we get closer to Christmas you can find more and more tiny red jewels. Green soldiers guard them with sharp weapons. What about carpets? Don't forget those. They are always changing this time of year. There's the soft brown one, the white glittery one and the tickly, prickly green one."

Jade had been quiet the whole of the walk, only smiling occasionally, but when they got back home she turned to her mum and said, "So things change all the time?"

"Yes darling they have to, but good new things come out of those changes and there are other things that will never change... I will always love you so much. That will never change." And she held Jade tight.

1. What do you think is/are the:

    a. nude ones?
    b. red, yellow and brown butterflies?
    c. tiny red jewels guarded by green soldiers with sharp pointed weapons?
    d. soft brown carpet?
    e. white glittery carpet?
    f. tickly, prickly green carpet?

2. What/which experience/s do you think that the writer may have had that has/have influenced this writing?

Name _____

Shut your mouth when you're eating

Shut your mouth when you're eating.
   I am, Dad.
MOUTH!
   It *is* shut.
I can *see* it isn't. I can *hear* it isn't.
   What about *his* mouth? You can *see* *everything* in his mouth.
He's only two. He doesn't know any better.
   You can see all his peas and tomato sauce.
That's none of your business.

(2 MINUTES GO BY)

   Dad.
Yes.
   Your mouth's open. Shut your mouth when you're eating.
It is shut, thank you very much.
   I can see it isn't, Dad. I can see all the food in there.
Look that's my business, OK?
   Peas, gravy, spuds everything.
Look, you don't want to grow up to be as horrible as your
father do you? Answer that, smartyboots.

by Michael Rosen

1. Which of the words below describe the form and style of this poem?
   Underline them.

   comedy, rhyming, limerick, prose (like writing a story), conversational, rap,
   epitaph

2. How is the author feeling and why?

3. There are three people in the poem, the author, the author's dad and one other.
   Who do you think the third person is?

4. What time of day do you think it is? How do you know?

5. Do you like this poem? Why/why not?

Name _____

Jabberwocky

'Twas brillig, and the slithy toves
    Did gyre and gimble in the wabe:
        All mimsy were the borogroves,
            And the mome raths outgrabe.

"Beware the Jabberwock, my son!
    The jaws that bite, the claws that catch!
        Beware the Jubjub bird, and shun
            The frumious Bandersnatch!"

He took his vorpal sword in hand:
    Long time the manxome foe he sought –
        So rested he by the Tumtum tree,
            And stood awhile in thought.

And, as in uffish thought he stood,
    The Jabberwock, with eyes of flame,
        Came whiffling through the tulgey wood,
            And burbled as it came!

Lewis Carroll

1. List all the nouns in this poem (nonsense words included).

2. List all the verbs in this poem (nonsense words included).

3. List all the adjectives in this poem (nonsense words included).

4. Underline all the words that describe the form and style of this poem:

   nonsense   narrative   rhyming   limerick   prose   conversational

5. Draw the scene as it stands now in the poem from the sense you can make of it. (What you are not told of the Jabberwock's appearance you may make up yourself.)

6. Write an explanation of the poem excerpt above for someone who doesn't understand it.

Name _____

Class register

❏ Read these names and see if you agree with the description of each person.

M.Blem (he has hundreds of badges!)

L.Bow (he is always pushing people out of the way!)

N.Choir (is always asking questions!)

C.Crett (she is quiet and you can't tell what she is thinking!)

I.Dear (he is always solving problems!)

D.Feet (she always gives up when things get a bit hard!)

Y.Lee (is clever but sneaky and cunning!)

B.Leeve (is really gullible!)

A.Ling (is always ill!)

O.Pinion (always has to have her say!)

C.Rious (hasn't got much of a sense of humour!)

I.See (isn't very friendly!)

A.Sing (is really good at tennis!)

O.Wing (is always borrowing things from people and never gives them back!)

E.Venning (is not a morning person!)

❏ Now put these names into a class list adding your own comments in brackets as above:

O.Bay   Y.Nerr   X.Pert   E.Ting   D.Light   D.Monn   E.Zee   E.Girly
D.Pendable   D.Manding   A.Bull   Q.Tee   X.Press   D.Fender

Name _____

Spy codes

❑ In order to keep written messages a secret they can be written in code. This means the words are changed somehow. This could be done in any number of ways but three codes are explained below.

The scramble code – The letters of each word are jumbled up (in the wrong order) and have to be rearranged to make sense. An example of a scrambled message is 'syp tuffs si loco'.

Dummy letter – An extra letter is added to the word and needs to be ignored for it to make sense. An example of a dummy letter message is 'sply stuffs tis crool'.

Swop letters – One letter in each word has been swopped for a letter in the next word. (You need to have a message with an even number of words in it for this code, of course.) An example of this code is 'sps tuffy ic sool'.

1. What do all the example coded messages above say?

   _____

2. Translate the following four fictional spy messages. What do they say? Which of the codes above did you need to use?

   Message 1 – They plackage tis rin sbox threem.

   _____

   Message 2 – teem em ta dimtighn dernu het drigeb.

   _____

   Message 3 – Hi es en tho lest plana ti Ameroca nomorrow tight?

   _____

   Message 4 – hes si yatsing ta rofu koa reet vider.

   _____

3. Using the codes above encode your own spy messages and give them to a friend to work out.

Name _____

Nail-biting finish for great rivals

❑ Complete the following report by writing appropriate words in the spaces.

On Saturday 10th July, Herne Hill Tennis Club was the venue for one of the _____ tennis matches that this reporter has ever seen. Herne Hill has won Division One for the last four years and their opponents were their great rivals, Tankerton, who have come second for the last four years. Both teams were _____ to win. Neither team had lost a match so far.

In the first of the four rubbers, Herne Hill's Peter Shurshott and Christina Smasher played Tankerton's Andy Chaser and Gill Litouch. It was a three set thriller. Tankerton won the first set 6–4 and then lost the second to the same score. The final set went all the way with a 13–11 tie-break finish making the final set 7–6 to Tankerton. "That was so _____," said Litouch.

In the second of the _____ rubbers Herne Hill badly needed a win. Rosalyn Smakkit and Howard Determin had to beat Tankerton's Tim Gottawin and Caroline Effert. It was another titanic fight. 6-3 to Tankerton in the first set but Herne Hill came fighting back to take the second set 6-2 with Determin dominating at the net. The Tankerton pair put up a good fight but went down 6-4 in the final set. "Howard was _____ on the net!" said Smakkit.

The third rubber saw the challengers, Tankerton, manage to get only two games! They were overpowered 0-6, 2-6 by returns that were inch perfect and by Shurshott's serve which swerved all over the place. "It was so _____ to return Peter's serve!" said a disappointed Gottawin.

The fourth and deciding rubber saw a nervous start by the Herne Hill pair. Tankerton took the first set 6-1. Herne Hill fought back in the second set though and the score became 4-4. The next game was going to be _____. Determin served well but lost it after five deuces and then, sensing victory, Chaser served the set out convincingly for Tankerton.

1. One feature that identifies this as a 'recounted text' is its chronological sequence. One of the words that illustrates this from the text is 'first'. What are the others?

2. What was the score in rubbers?

3. What was the score in sets?

4. What was the score in games?

5. So who won?

Name _____

Recipe for special swirl biscuits

❑ The recipe below was written for a person with food allergies.

225g wheat-free flour
1 tsp baking powder
85g non-dairy margarine
5 tbsp date syrup
Three drops of almond essence

It is difficult to find sweet foods that do not
have manufactured sugar in them. Here is a
delicious biscuit that is sweet because of the
date syrup, which, of course, is a pure fruit syrup
and contains no added sugar. Some supermarkets
now have alternatives to dairy and wheat foods.
If you have trouble getting hold of any of these
ingredients just ask at a wholefood store.

1. Preheat the oven to 160 degrees Celsius/325 degrees Fahrenheit/gas mark 3.
2. First measure out the flour and baking powder and sift them together. (Two
    little tips for you: Remember to hold the sieve high over the bowl to add air
    to the mixture and you could use rice flour in this recipe but you will probably
    find that you need to use a little more baking powder in order to make the
    biscuits light. Try an extra half a teaspoon.)
3. Next measure out the margarine and rub it together with the flour using your
    finger tips until the mixture is like fine breadcrumbs.
4. Now measure the date syrup and almond essence and stir them into the
    mixture. It should hold together enough for you to make slightly tacky balls in
    your palm. (Little tip: If it doesn't, carefully add up to another tablespoon of
    the date syrup until you achieve this.)
5. Now break off balls of the mixture that are golf ball size and squash them
    flat to about a centimetre thickness.
6. Place them on a greased baking sheet with space between them and cook them
    in the centre of the oven for 15 to 20 minutes until they are quite firm to the
    touch on top.
7. Remove from the baking sheet and cool on a wire rack before putting them in
    an airtight container.

1. The above recipe was put together for a person with food allergies.
    Which foods is it clear the person cannot have?

2. Draw labelled diagrams to show each step in the recipe.

Name _____

Scrambled instructions

❑ Below is a set of instructions on how to tie shoelaces but they are in the wrong order.

❑ First cut out the separate instructions and put them in the right order. Then number them and stick them, correctly ordered, onto a new piece of paper. Do an illustration for each one.

Hold one end of the shoelace still and take the other end under the bit of lace above it and through the hole.

As you pull it through it will form a second loop as the bow tightens.

Pull both ends tight – this is a half knot. Let go of both ends.

Take hold of both loop ends and pull tight.

Hold one end of the shoelace an inch from the tip and make a loop by putting your hand up to the half knot and so folding the lace.

Cross the two ends of the shoelace over to make an 'x' shape. Let go of both ends.

Now hold the other end of the lace half way down and wrap it all the way around the loop and through the hole just above the half knot.

Name _____

What is it?

❑ Follow the instructions below. You will need a pencil and rubber.

Faintly draw a large circle below. Divide the circle into quarters. Now pushing hard with the pencil bold half the circle. Pushing hard with your pencil again draw a series of about six little bridge shapes in the circle. Now draw a thick capital 'J' shape without the top stroke to the bottom of the circle. Now carefully rub out the faint lines that you can still see.

❑ The instructions were for drawing an umbrella. You have probably realised that they could be better. Rewrite the instructions making them more clear.

_____

_____

_____

_____

_____

_____

Name _____

Titanic

Titanic was the name given to the largest moving object that had ever been built. More than 11,300 shipworkers worked for 26 months to build her. British people thought it was marvellous. It was described as 'a floating palace'. The rooms were very stylish and there were lavish facilities including a swimming pool, gymnasium and barber's shop. It had all the most advanced safety features it could have. Everybody thought it was unsinkable.

Titanic began her maiden (first) voyage from Southampton on 10 April 1912. There was a huge celebration as she sailed off covered in colourful decorations. There was a party mood on board and passengers were very excited. However four days into the voyage, just before midnight, a lookout (a person positioned high up on the ship in order to look for danger) saw an iceberg ahead. Titanic began to turn but hit the iceberg and had holes ripped in its hull below the waterline. Water rushed into the ship. Titanic was definitely going to sink because of the damage caused.

But so strong was the belief that Titanic was unsinkable, that while some of the crew were trying to organise people into the lifeboats, others were saying there was no need to panic. There were not enough lifeboats for all the people on board, only about half. Women and children were put in the lifeboats first. Many lifeboats were lowered the 20 metres to the water before they were full.

Titanic sent out distress calls by wireless, by Morse lamp and by firing distress rockets into the air that shot upwards and were very bright. A ship could be seen in the distance and people hoped that it would come to their rescue, but it didn't. It sailed away. About two hours and 40 minutes after hitting the iceberg Titanic sank into the water with many passengers still on board. Light shone through the portholes until it sank, so the survivors could see the ship clearly. Some people jumped from the ship and tried to get to the lifeboats. The water was freezing.

Carpathia, the ship rushing to Titanic's aid, didn't get to them until morning. The night would have been very cold and dark. 2,228 passengers started the voyage... only 705 of them survived to land at New York.

❑ Imagine you were a passenger enjoying a drink in the lounge when the ship struck the iceberg. Use the facts above to describe what happened to you from the minute before Titanic struck the iceberg to your escape to a lifeboat and long wait until you were eventually rescued by the ship Carpathia. Describe the mood on the Titanic, your feelings and the scene around you.

PHOTOCOPIABLE ....

COMPREHENSION BOOK 3 19

Name _____

Make a mask

❏ This mask below is called a 'Rangda' mask. Rangda is an evil character in many
stories in Asia. Write a set of instructions, with illustrations, for someone of your
age to make this mask. Start with a list of the materials needed.

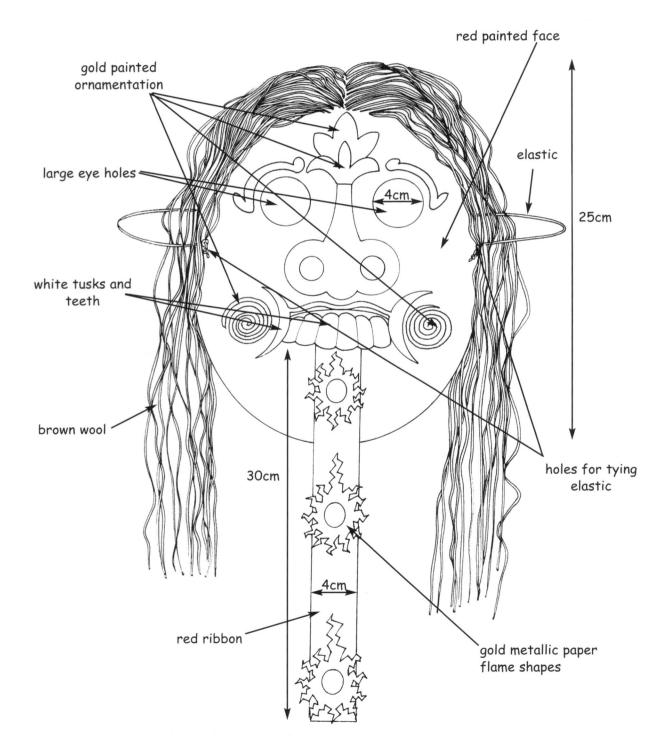

red painted face

gold painted
ornamentation

elastic

large eye holes

4cm

25cm

white tusks and
teeth

brown wool

holes for tying
elastic

30cm

4cm

red ribbon

gold metallic paper
flame shapes

Name _____

The taxi company

❏ A taxi firm is operating in the area shown on the map below. All the taxi drivers are new to the area having come from another company. A call comes in from Miss Spent at Tesco. She wants to go home. Her address is 4 Market Road. A second call comes in from Mr Chuffa who wants to be picked up from home and taken to the train station. His address is 18 Carriage Close. A third call comes in from Mrs Christian who wants to go from her home to church. Her address is 21 Cross Lane.

❏ First, decide which taxi is closest to each pick-up and so should take which fare. Then write out the directions that would have to be given to each taxi.

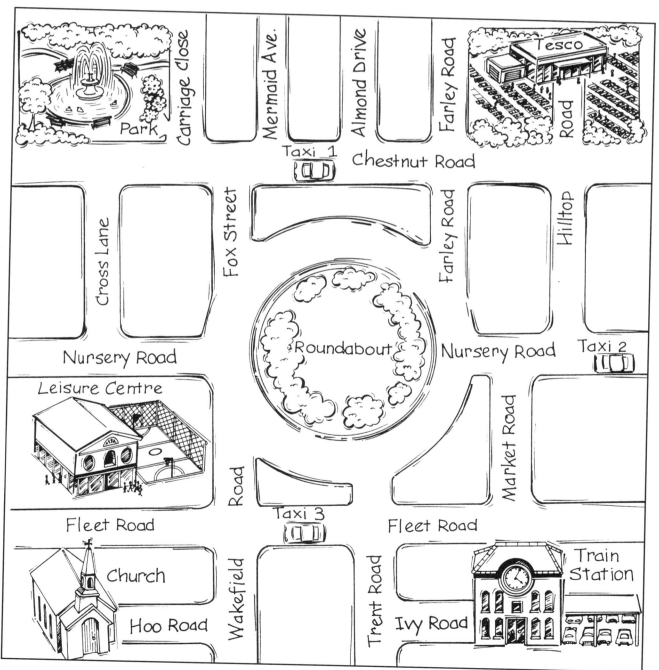

Name _____

Train timetable

☐ Miss Actin wants to go to the theatre in London and go back on the same day. The show starts at 2.30pm and finishes at 4.45pm. She is going to get on the train at Whitstable. Two sections of the train timetable for the day she wants to go are shown below.

Ramsgate	0815	0852	0922	0959	1022
Chestfield and Swalecliffe	0845	0922	0952	------	1052
Whitstable	0848	0926	0956	1026	1056
Sittingbourne	0911	0947	1017	1047	1117
Chatham	0928	1003	1033	1103	1133
Longfield	0946	------	------	------	------
London Victoria	1018	1047	1117	1147	1217

London Victoria	1804	1834	1904	1934	1934
Longfield	------	------	------	------	------
Chatham	1855	1917	1946	2017	2017
Sittingbourne	1912	1934	2002	2032	2032
Whitstable	1933	1954	2024	2053	------
Chestfield and Swalecliffe	1936	1957	------	2056	------
Ramsgate	------	2030	2055	2128	------

☐ Using the information above, instruct Miss Actin about the trains she could catch.

1. If Miss Actin wants to get to London Victoria by midday, so she can have some lunch, what are her options?

2. If Miss Actin also wants to go with a friend, Miss Directa who would get on at Chestfield, what options has she then?

3. If Miss Directa decides she can't get to the station before half past nine in the morning, which train do they have to take?

4. The two ladies think they can get back to London Victoria station an hour after the show finishes. Which trains can they catch home?

5. If they now decide to spend at least an hour in the station bar having a drink and a snack which train do they have to catch?

Name _____

Going camping

❑ Below is a diagram of all the things it is recommended you should take in a backpack when going on a camping trip.

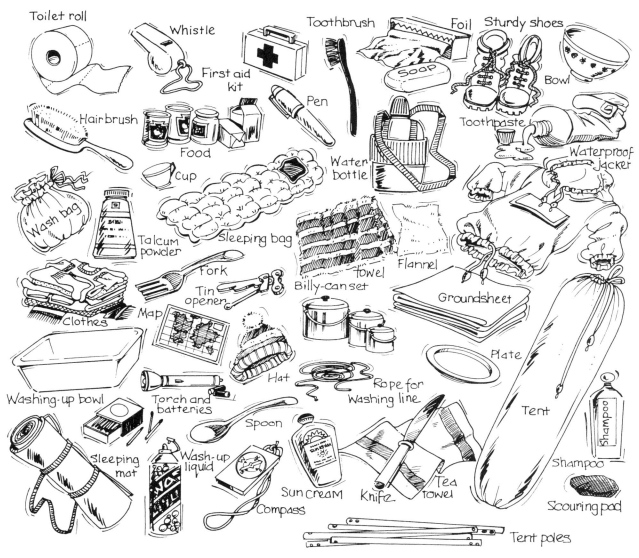

1. From the information above, instruct someone who is going camping for the first time as to what they should take. List the items under the appropriate one of these five headings: wash kit; washing up kit; cooking kit; shelter kit and survival kit.

2. Why do you think the following things are recommended for campers?
   a) The backpack is lined with bin-liners.
   b) The first aid kit is in the side pocket, rather than the main part of the backpack.
   c) Items are packed inside each other where possible.
   d) A whistle should be worn at all times.
   e) Sturdy shoes are worn, rather than flimsy ones.

PHOTOCOPIABLE ....

COMPREHENSION BOOK 3   23

Name _____

Earthquakes

❏ The following passages are selected parts of letters describing people's experiences of four different earthquakes.

(Earthquake 1)
We were in the lounge at the time of the earthquake. It felt like a huge lorry was passing right by us. A few things fell off the table and shelves. Everybody indoors felt it but some people who had been outside had not noticed it.

(Earthquake 2)
I can hardly bear to think about it. Almost all the buildings in the street just crumbled to the ground. One minute they were there and the next minute there was a huge rumbling and the ground moved like a wave and cracked apart. There was total devastation. There were fires everywhere because the gas pipes and the electricity cables broke. There was chaos with survivors running and screaming for help.

(Earthquake 3)
The ground trembled. Everyone felt it. Everything shook. Our fence broke and bricks fell from the chimney and tiles fell off the roof. When we went back into the house we found the plaster walls had cracked and there were things all over the floor. It was the same in all the houses in the street.

(Earthquake 4)
Five of the houses in our street just fell to the ground. All the other houses including ours were left cracked and broken. There was a fire at the end of the street where a gas pipe had broken and come up out of the ground.

❏ The Mercalli scale calculates the strength or intensity of an earthquake by assessing the damage it causes. You are going to make a similar scale.

❏ Summarise each of the four paragraphs into a statement of damage caused by the earthquake and put these four statements into order from the least severe earthquake to the most severe. Draw a picture to go with each statement.

Name _____

Legend of a wise man

A long time ago a boy was born. His parents knew he was wise from a very early age. As a baby he never cried (as he knew this would upset his parents) but instead gurgled for attention and then pointed to various parts of his body to tell them what he needed: his mouth for food; his eyes for sleep and of course his bottom for toilet! Soon the baby began to talk and friends and family began to come to him for advice. Everyone in the village heard about this and they too began to come to him for advice. Then word spread (as it tends to) to other villages and soon the whole kingdom was coming to him for advice. (He could have made a fortune if he had ever asked for payment – personally speaking I think he was unwise in this!) When the boy had grown into a man, the queue outside his house was miles long. He was giving advice all day long and nothing else was getting done. One day when the wise man was asked for advice he paused and then said, "What do you think?" The people were puzzled at first and then grew angry. "How selfish of him not to help us!" The wise man was exiled and never heard from again. Years later when the kingdom was prosperous again the people realised what the wise man had done for them and started telling the tale to honour him.

1. There should be four paragraphs in this story. The beginning of the first paragraph is the beginning of the story. Put a vertical line in the text to show where you think the second, third and fourth paragraphs should begin.

2. Why do you think the wise man stopped giving advice?

3. Do you think the wise man was being selfish? Why/why not?

4. Why was the tale told to honour the wise man?

Name _____

A happy ending and a sad ending

There were two birds that lived in a wood. The weather grew worse every day and every day it became harder and harder to find food. One day the two birds met at the frozen lake.

"It's so awful. No water to drink. I'm so thirsty," said the first bird.

"Yes, but it's good fun to skate on. Come on," said the second and glided across the ice. The first bird shook his head and walked away.

The next day the two birds met in a tree.

"It's so awful. This hail hurts so much when you're flying in it," said the first bird.

"Yes, but I like the rhythms it makes when it hits the leaves. Dance with me," said the second bird. The first bird shook his head and left the second bird to dance on his own.

On the last day of their lives the two birds met under a bush.

"It's so awful. This wind cuts right through me," said the first bird weakly.

"Yes, but it's fun to stop flying and just have a ride on it," said the second bird, "come on. One last ride."

The first bird shook his head and lay down. The second bird had one last ride and then returned to the bush and lay down next to the first bird.

1. What time of year is it?

2. Describe the first bird's character.

3. Describe the second bird's character.
.
4. Do you think this story can teach us anything? If so, what?

Name _____

Who rules the forest?

❑ Cut out the four story parts shown. Put them in order so that the story makes sense. Then glue them onto another sheet of paper and draw three pictures to show how the small animals solved the tasks.

Next, the animals gathered around a huge fallen tree by a river. "Remember," said the monkey, "the tree has to be moved at least ten tree lengths." The gorilla laughed and hugged the tree. He heaved and heaved and did manage to lift it but soon had to put it down again. "None of you small animals can do this!" As soon as he said that, the beavers went to the tree and pushed and pushed until it rolled into the river. Then they slid into the water after it and guided it down the river for ten tree lengths. The larger animals couldn't believe it.

A huge boulder was then tied with strong vines and attached to a tree that grew at the top of a hill. "Now remember," said the monkey, "for this final task you only need to move the boulder the distance of three of my feet." The gorilla laughed and grabbed the rope near the tree. He pulled and pulled but the boulder didn't move at all. "None of you small animals can do this!" As soon as he said that, the wild mice ran to the tree and nibbled at the vines. The boulder rolled the length of three of the monkey's feet to the bottom of the hill. So the monkey became King of the forest and he made a committee of small and large animals to help him.

One day, all the animals gathered in the forest to decide who should be in charge. The largest animals sat together and whispered together. Then the gorilla stood up and said in a loud voice, "The forest needs strong rulers. I am the strongest of all so I will be King!" The small animals got together and whispered for a while and then the monkey spoke in a calm assured voice. "We have thought of three tasks that we think a good king should be able to complete." He told the large animals what they were and they all burst into uncontrollable laughter. "I will complete those tasks on my own. All of you small animals put together will not be able to do better!" boasted the gorilla.

All the animals gathered around a huge pit into which the monkey had been lowered. "Now remember," said the monkey, "In this first task, whoever rescues me from this pit can use only their own strength or strengths." The gorilla laughed and jumped into the pit next to the monkey. "Jump on my back cousin. Hold tight around my neck, I'll have you out of here in a minute." The gorilla tried jumping and climbing and jumping and climbing but he couldn't get out of the pit. Eventually he gave up. "None of you small animals can do this!" As soon as he said this the snakes tied themselves together heads to tails and the first snake wrapped himself around a nearby tree. The snakes at the other end slithered down into the pit. The last snake wrapped himself around the monkey and then all the snakes heaved the monkey out of the pit. The larger animals couldn't believe it.

Name _____

Snappy's story

His lovely, peaceful seaside home!

He wanted to enjoy it all on his own

A picturesque sheltered little bay

If only those noisy kids would just go _____

You might find him in the shallow water

Waiting for the unwary son or _____

Or perhaps behind the sandcastle

Waiting to get that dirty _____

If they stepped on a clump of weed

He was going to make them _____

Hidden under an overturned spade

They had every right to be _____

At any hiding place he may be there

Parents tell your noisy children _____

He was undisputed King of the beach

There wasn't a toe he could not _____

Until the day they each turned up with a line

We can only wonder if he knew it was his _____

Now you'll understand the word irony when I tell you of his fate

For a noisy child went quiet and smiled when he looked upon his plate.

1. Complete the poem by writing the missing words that follow the rhyming pattern.

2. Who or what is Snappy?

3. Draw a picture of Snappy in the box.

4. According to the poem, in which places at the seaside could he be found?

5. What happened to Snappy in the end?

Name _____

It wasn't my fault

I normally wear glasses you see

But I left them at home on the settee

Yes. The windscreen is a bit dirty

Look... it's a good job I was doing less than thirty

He came right out of nowhere

He should have been driving with care

The man's driving nearly killed me

You know I've only just turned forty

Yes. I know it was a police van

Yes. I know the driver's a policeman

I'm sorry he's hurt his neck

Look... my car's a wreck

Officer I've nothing to hide...

Was he really parked at the roadside?

❑ The writer and a policeman were involved in the incident the writer is talking about. Fill out a police report for this incident using the details in the poem. Use these headings:

Number and details of vehicles involved

Number and details of people involved

Statements from each person involved

Additional relevant information

Name _____

The beast within

Carol had been found wandering along the road from Tilburn Forest to the Star 25 nightclub. She looked shaken as though she'd been through something terrible. She had been taken to the hospital. It took two days for the psychologists to help her to talk. When she did she told them of the horror she had been through. She and her boyfriend had been driving home from a nightclub down the road that went through Tilburn Forest. It was about midnight. They had broken down. Their mobile battery was low. Her

boyfriend had got out of the car to try and flag down another vehicle. After a while he decided it wasn't likely there would be another car down the road so he tried to fix the car himself. He'd managed only to gash his hand badly. They had decided to start walking back to the club. The road was dimly lit so she had taken a torch with them. They had gone about a mile when from somewhere near them in the trees they heard a dreadful growl. They ran for the club but had only taken a few steps when a dark shadow like a large cat leapt out at her boyfriend and knocked him over. She had tried to hit it with the torch but in the confusion she had hit her boyfriend. The beast bit into Jaz's chest and dragged him off into the forest screaming. Then the screaming became fainter and finally stopped. She couldn't remember anything after that.

The police searched every inch of the huge forest. There was no sign of Jaz's body. They found the torch broken and bloody by the side of the road next to some bloodstains and some signs that Jaz had been dragged into the forest but the trail seemed to just stop after a while. They found the car and more of Jaz's blood in the engine and on the road just by it. They found no footprints at all near the torch, not even of the wild deer that lived in the forest. As it was January and the ground was rock hard that was what the forensic examiner had expected. The police also discovered that Jaz and Carol had been arguing badly before they left the Star 25 club that night. Jaz's parents told the police about Carol's terrible temper and about the times she had hit him.

Carol was charged with murder. An open verdict was recorded.

1. What evidence do you think was offered to prove Carol innocent of the crime?

2. What evidence do you think was offered to prove Carol guilty of the crime?

3. Which features of the story do you think best identify it as a mystery story?

Name _____

Solo flight

Ann got out of the lift at level nine and walked to the flight school canteen. She stood in front of the scanner. The blue light passed across her face.

"Which foods do you require?" came the happy computer voice.

"Meal three," she said.

As she sat down by the window she looked at her synthetic food. It never tasted very good to her. She longed for some fresh vegetables, fruit and meat like the ancients used to eat. It was very hard to get those foods now. The ancients had ruined the surface. The Earth became hot and dry because of all the greenhouse gases polluting the atmosphere, and the hole in the ozone layer had become so large many ancients had died of skin cancer. The ancients knew that when the polar ice caps melted only the highest mountain ranges of Earth would be safe. Everywhere else would be flooded. There had been a terrible nuclear war over this land. The last ancients had built cities underground with their own oxygen systems and moved into them before the ice caps melted. Each city was now called a state. There were only 40 states in the whole world. The last ancients had taken everything they could from the surface but there had been very little good water left.

Ann took a sip from her body suit. They all had to wear these suits under their clothes all the time. It recycled and cleaned the water from their bodies so they could drink it. She would never forget the first time she had been taken in a jet up through the huge metal doors to the surface. She had seen rivers and the sea. So much water! Apart from the pilots, only miners and panel workers were allowed on the surface and they had to wear heavy metal suits. The radiation levels were still a bit high. Tomorrow would be her first solo flight. She couldn't wait. She had no idea how disastrous those solo flights could be.

1. Is the story set in the past, present or future?

2. Where in the world is the flight school?

3. Who or what gave Ann her food?

4. What did Ann drink? Why did she have to do this?

5. Who were 'the ancients'?

6. Why did the miners and panel workers wear heavy metal suits?

7. What was Ann training to become?

Name _____

My mum's mad!

❏ Read the poem below. Discuss with a partner what you think the figures of speech that are underlined really mean. On another sheet of paper, draw pictures to show what you think.

My mum says <u>I have ants in my pants</u>… but I've never seen them!
My mum says <u>I spill the beans</u>… but I never have!
My mum says <u>I'm always getting in a stew</u>… but I wouldn't do that – too messy!
My mum says <u>I lead her on wild goose chases</u>… but there aren't any round here!
My mum says <u>I'm full of hot air</u>… but that would make me float away!

❏ Match each of the five examples of everyday experiences below to the correct one of the five figures of speech and the correct one of the five actual meanings.

Actual meanings

A. Making someone really mad.
B. Doing something to hurt someone even though it will hurt you as well.
C. Being sure about something that you shouldn't be.
D. Being really fussy about something and saying it's not quite right.
E. Getting someone to follow your advice even though it's not right.

Examples of everyday experiences

1. Saying you're going to pass a test tomorrow.
2. If your tennis partner has upset you and you say you won't play the last game with them.
3. Winding someone up.
4. Pretending to someone that you are a driving instructor and taking money off them for lessons.
5. Saying that a toy is a slightly different shade of blue than it looked in the catalogue.

Figures of speech

i) 'Leading someone down the garden path'
ii) 'Making someone see red'
iii) 'Splitting hairs'
iv) 'Cutting off your nose to spite your face'
v) 'Counting your chickens before they are hatched'

Name _____

A Greek myth

❏ The comic strip below shows a Greek myth about a creature known as a Cyclops who has only one eye. His name is Polyphemus. He looked after a flock of sheep and lived in a cave. The story also has a hero named Odysseus.

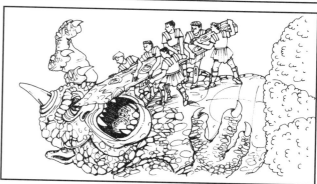

❏ Use the comic strip to write your own version of the Greek myth.

Name _____

No sense at all

God had made a beautiful world with things in it to delight every sense. There was also everything that man would need to live well and all of it was free.

But man wanted more, so he started changing things. He invented a system he called 'wealth'. The people who were the wealthiest had the most man-made things. Soon everyone wanted to be the wealthiest. They prayed to God for more wealth. God said they could have more wealth but for not appreciating what he had given them he would take away all but one texture in the world.

The people agreed and they became very wealthy but everything in the world felt the

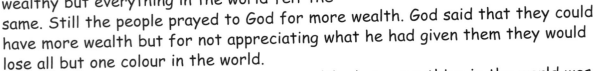

same. Still the people prayed to God for more wealth. God said that they could have more wealth but for not appreciating what he had given them they would lose all but one colour in the world.

They agreed and became very, very wealthy but everything in the world was the same colour. Still the people prayed to God for more wealth. God said they could become wealthier but for not appreciating what he had given them he would take away all but one fragrance in the world.

They agreed and became very, very, very wealthy but everything in the world smelled the same. Still the people prayed to God for more wealth. God said they could have more wealth but for not appreciating what he had given them he would take away all but one sound in the world.

They agreed and became very, very, very, very wealthy but everything in the world sounded the same. As the people looked around their ruined world they longed for the varied, natural textures, colours, smells and sounds they had once known. They prayed silently for God to forgive them. God did forgive them and the world became again as it had been in the beginning.

1. What lessons can be learned from this fable?

2. Which of the five senses is not specifically mentioned?

3. Underline the main points in each paragraph. Use these points to tell the story to a friend.

Name _____

Receding coastlines

❑ Our coastlines can change in many ways. Below are details of the four ways in which coasts recede (are 'eaten away').

Corrasion

This is the action of loose rocks being thrown at the bottom of cliffs by waves. This gradually carves out caves and eventually these caves will not be able to support the weight of the rock above and will collapse. This shortens the cliff.

Hydraulic Action

When waves crash against cliff faces they trap air in the crevices (cracks) there. The water squashes the air putting it under a lot of pressure. When the wave recedes, the pressure is released. The air then expands with explosive force and can break the rock further making the crevices bigger. Eventually the rock crumbles and shortens the cliff. Softer rock is therefore eroded at a faster rate.

Corrosion

This is the chemical action by which the seawater dissolves some rocks (like limestone).

Attrition

This is the action of loose rocks being ground (rubbed hard) together by the waves making them smaller and smaller. Soft rock like shale or moraine is therefore eroded at a faster rate.

❑ A teacher trying to teach a class the above information set up the following demonstrations. Work out which actions are being taught in which demonstration and draw a diagram for each one. Don't forget to put a title for each diagram (which action it is) and label the equipment to show what each piece represents.

  a. The teacher rubbed two sugar cubes together.

  b. The teacher put a sugar cube in a glass of warm water and stirred it.

  c. The teacher made a solid wall of wet sand and then threw small pebbles at the bottom of the wall.

  d. The teacher showed the class a blown-up balloon covered in wet sand so only a little of the balloon was showing. Then the teacher pushed on this part of the balloon to squash it and then released it immediately.

Name _____

Volcanoes

Volcanoes are like mountains. Some are so tall that ice can form on the top. There is a hole at the top that is called a 'crater' and below the crater is a column called a 'vent pipe' which goes down through the earth's crust to molten (liquid) rock called 'magma' which is incredibly hot and under pressure i.e. being squashed. The volcano erupts when this 'magma' is under too much pressure and bursts through the earth and up the 'vent pipe' and 'crater', creating lots of gas and dust as well with the force of the explosion. From here it flows down the sides of the volcano and is called 'lava'. Any ice on the top of the volcano melts and this melted ice runs down the side of the volcano mixing with earth, ash and dust to create a mudflow called a 'lahar'.

❏ Draw and label a diagram of an erupting volcano that had ice on the top.

Name _____

The Victorians

❑ Below is a list of some of the characteristic aspects of Victorian life.

Previously people had worked on the land but in Victorian times a lot of people moved to the towns where new factories were being built everywhere. These factories were powered by steam.

Sanitation was still poor in that only the rich had the chance of proper toilets, running water or drains.

Goods were sold in the street from handcarts and in markets. There were few shops. Poor girls typically sold cut flowers and poor boys might shine shoes. Rich young ladies spent their life at social gatherings like balls, the theatre and opera This was so they could be seen by rich men who might want to marry them.

A person called Singer invented the sewing machine in 1851. This meant clothes could be mass-produced.

Another invention was the phonograph, which meant sounds could be recorded and played back. Thomas Edison was responsible for this in 1877.

The Education Act was passed. That meant all children had to go to school and that parents didn't need to pay for it. The classes were large and the teachers disciplined the children harshly, beating them to make them behave.

Tinned goods became available for the first time. Refrigerators were invented. Food was chilled by air cooled by ice blocks in a compartment next to the food.

If a person stole something or attacked someone they could be put to death. These are just two of over 70 crimes that were punishable by death. Towns had their own police force often consisting of men from the army.

For entertainment, people could choose from just a few things: football; tennis; cricket; prize fighting (no rules and fighting with bare fists); visits to the town parks; trips to the music hall (where they could see juggling, comedy acts and singers) and once rail travel became cheaper, days at the seaside.

1. Underline in red all the aspects of Victorian life that we still have today.

2. Underline in blue all the aspects of Victorian life that no longer exist.

3. Why do you think that lots of Victorians moved from the country to the towns?

4. In which century could clothes be mass-produced?

5. Which words are today's equivalent of these Victorian terms:

   phonograph   **music hall**   **omnibus**

Name ——————————————

Aztec Eagle Knight

The Aztecs were always looking for new areas to conquer and add to their empire and they wanted to capture enemy warriors to use as human sacrifices in their religious ceremonies. Aztec warriors who showed courage in battle were greatly respected and given distinctive costumes with jaguar and eagle designs. The more captives they took the more elaborate the costume.

The Eagle Knight's costume was made from leather and was covered in feathers. It had a helmet shaped like an eagle's head with an open beak. When this helmet was worn, the warrior's head was in the open beak. There were wings on the arms of the costume like an eagle's.

Imitation (fake) talons were worn around the knees. The shield was round and made of leather. It often had bright feathers dangling from the bottom in strands. One of the main weapons was a war club called a 'maquahuitl'. It was about 76 centimetres long and looked like a cricket bat. The broader part had grooved sides which had sharp (volcanic) glass blades embedded in it. The legs of the costume came down to about the knees. They wore leather sandals on their feet.

❏ Draw a picture of the Aztec Eagle Knight described above and then label it.

Name _____

Aztec life

❑ This is an extract from an information book about the life of a people called the Aztecs who lived about 800 years ago in the high valleys of what we now call Mexico.

The Aztecs lived in cities. Within each city Aztecs lived in small family groups called 'calpullis'. They each had a headman. The head men from the noble families elected a ruler called the 'Tlatoani' which means **great speaker**. This man ruled the city. He was both a priest and a brave warrior.

Many Aztec houses had a separate **sweat-room**. They were built from stone. Fires were lit around the outside walls to heat it. Inside, the Aztecs would splash water on to the hot walls to make steam. Once the Aztecs were sweating they would plunge into the nearest stream or pool.

The Aztecs used **pictograms** when they wanted to write things down. Several pictograms could be joined together to make a sentence. These pictograms were written on folded deerskin or **codex**.

One of the two main games played by the Aztecs was **tlachtli**. Two teams attempt to score by propelling a solid rubber ball through rings set eight metres high on the walls of specially made courts. The court represented the world and the ball represented the Moon and the Sun. The rings were decorated, some with animals like snakes and monkeys. It was a dangerous game because the ball was very hard and was propelled at great speed. Bets were placed on the game and some people lost everything they had – sometimes their lives!

1. Write dictionary entries for the terms and words above that are printed in bold, putting them in alphabetical order and explaining them in your own words.

2. Now, from the list of modern-day terms below find the one best match for each of the terms or words in bold:

   Mayor, Prime Minister, King, paper, computer, sauna, jacuzzi, bath, words, letters, paragraphs, basketball, football and volleyball.

Name _____

Sounds

One way to describe a sound is its pitch, which means how high (screechy) or low (deep) the sound is. A scream is a high-pitched sound and men tend to have lower pitched (deeper) voices than women. A drum tends to make a sound that is low-pitched and a flute tends to make a high-pitched sound. The pitch of a sound is a measure of how fast the source of the sound is vibrating. If the source of the sound is vibrating very quickly the sound is high pitched. If the vibrations are slower the pitch of the sound is lower. The sources of sounds that are smallest, shortest, thinnest, lightest and tightest will have the highest pitched sounds. For instance, the smallest bars on a xylophone have the highest pitch.

Another way to describe a sound is its volume which means how loud (high volume) or quiet (low volume) it is. Volume is a measure of how strong or weak the vibrations are. The closer to the source of sound you are the stronger the vibrations will be. Further away from the source of sound the vibrations will be weaker and the sound will be quieter. Also if you dampen the vibrations (make the vibrations weaker) the sound will be quieter and if you amplify the vibrations (make the vibrations stronger) the sound will be louder. For instance if you are playing a cymbal and you want to make the sound quieter you could hold the edge of it or put cotton wool in your ears as both weaken the vibrations reaching your ears. If you wanted to make it louder you could hit it harder or put a microphone near it, as both measures would make the vibrations reaching your ears stronger.

❑ Would the pitch of a guitar be lower or higher if you did each of the following?
1. Tighten all the strings.
2. Push your third finger down across all the strings half way up its neck.
3. Swap all the strings for thicker ones.

❑ Your sister is playing the drums in the room next door. Which of the following things could you do to give the sound a lower volume?
a. Go to a room in another part of the house.
b. Put your pillow over your head.
c. Wrap a cloth around the end of the drumsticks.
d. Open your door.
e. Put a blanket in her large drum.
f. Put your ear to the wall between her room and yours.

❑ Divide a piece of paper into quarters and write one of these titles in each part: Low-pitched sounds; High-pitched sounds; Low volume sounds; High volume sounds. In each quarter draw pictures that are examples of that title. Use the ones in the text and then find more of your own. (Remember that a sound can belong under more than one title.)

Name _____

The planets

❑ Earth is one of nine planets orbiting the Sun.

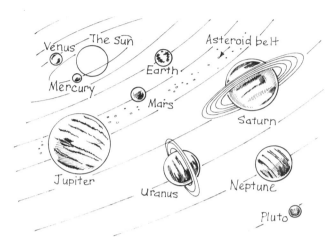

Mercury: This is a small planet. Its diameter is about 4,878km. It has no air or water so nothing can live there. As a young planet it was bombarded by huge space rocks called asteroids, so it has a battered surface and looks like a walnut. It takes 88 days to orbit the Sun.

Venus: It has a diameter of about 12,100km. It is a terrifying world of volcanoes and lava lakes and has poisonous gases around it that trap the Sun's heat and make it the hottest of all the planets. These clouds also prevent light reaching the surface and make the planet gloomy (dark).

Earth: It is covered in land and water and is blue and green. Its diameter is about 12,756km. It has millions of different living organisms on it including humans.

Mars: Mars is about 6,794km in diameter. Much of Mars is dry, rocky desert. It appears red in colour. It is a much colder planet than Earth.

Jupiter: This is the largest of all the planets (diameter 142,984km). It is a ball of gas clouds and has no solid surface. It has streaks and swirls across it, which are caused by winds and storms.

Saturn: This planet has bright rings of ice and rock around it. Like Jupiter it is a giant planet made up of gas but it does have a centre of rock that is about the same size as Earth. The planet is about 120,000km in diameter.

Uranus: This planet was discovered in 1781. It is a blue and green ball of gas and water but has a molten rock centre. Its diameter is about 52,000km.

Neptune: Neptune is another planet of gas and water. It is a blue ball with very dark rings and many white clouds. It has the strongest winds in the solar system. Its diameter is about 48,400km. It is 4,496,700,000km away from the Sun.

Pluto: Scientists think this planet is made up of rock, ice and frozen gas but little is known about it. It looks a bit like an asteroid. It is a very small planet, only about 2,445km in diameter.

❑ Design a chart to show the planets in order of their size from smallest to largest. Write in the chart key words from the information above to describe the appearance of each one and how close it is to the Sun in relation to the other planets.

Name _____

Silly survey

❑ A teacher, Mr Veryfare, was doing a lesson on bar charts and decided to do a silly survey to make it more fun. He asked each of the children to imagine themselves doing the following things:

Putting their feet into boots filled with jelly.
Having a bath in cold baked beans.
Having a bowl of cold spaghetti poured over their head.
Getting an apple out of a bucket of rice pudding using their teeth.

❑ Mr Veryfare asked each of them to say which one they would choose to do if they had to do one of the options. The results are on the bar chart below.

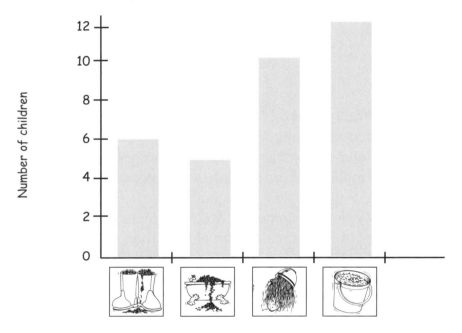

1. Which option was least popular?

2. Which option was most popular?

3. How many more children preferred to put their feet in boots filled with jelly than to have a bath of cold baked beans?

4. How many children were there in the class?

❑ The same survey was then done in another class of 28 children.
Five children would prefer to put their feet in boots filled with jelly.
Nine children would prefer to have a bath in cold baked beans.
Seven children would prefer to have a bowl of cold spaghetti poured over their head.

5. How many children preferred to get an apple out of a bucket of rice pudding using their teeth?

6. Plot the results of this other class on a bar chart.

Name _____

Pulse rate

The heart is a crucial organ. The ribs protect it. The heart acts as a pump pushing the blood around the body. This push is called blood pressure. Each time the heart beats (squeezes and pushes the blood out) a wave of blood flows along the arteries. The number of times this happens in a minute is called a pulse. If you turn your palm upwards and put your second and third fingers across the underside of your wrist you should feel the throb as the heart beats. If you count how many throbs (heart beats) there are in a minute this is your pulse. Your pulse at any one minute will probably be different to your friend's. If you are quite relaxed when you take your pulse it is called your resting pulse. If you now exercise, your muscles need to work harder. This means they need more oxygen, which is carried to the muscles by the blood pumped from the heart. This means that your pulse quickens (gets faster/higher) because your heart is pumping more blood. Then, when you stop, your pulse will gradually get slower (lower/smaller) and closer to your resting pulse again because your muscles aren't working so hard and the heart isn't pumping so much blood.

❑ A centre back on the football team, Di Namight, was fitted with a heart monitor to see how her pulse rate changed during a ten-minute period. Her resting pulse was found to be 68 beats per minute. The results are shown in the chart.

1. Plot a graph to illustrate the results.

2. In which minute of the match was she working hardest?

3. In which minute of the match did she work least hard?

4. Did she work harder in the first five minutes or the last five minutes?

5. Explain in your own words what a pulse rate is and why it changes frequently.

Minute	Pulse
First	68
Second	70
Third	74
Fourth	78
Fifth	74
Sixth	74
Seventh	80
Eighth	82
Ninth	80
Tenth	80

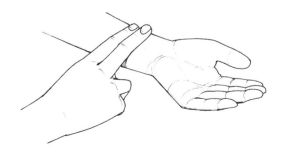

Name _____

When we exercise

When we exercise, our muscles need to work harder. In order for the muscles to work harder the muscle cells (tiny parts of the muscle) need more oxygen.

All the cells (tiny parts) of the body need to have oxygen to live, grow and produce energy for the body's activities.

So how does the oxygen get to the cells? The answer is that we breathe air into our lungs and it is here that the oxygen mixes with the blood and is carried along with it to the heart and is then pumped round to all parts of the body. (The lungs are like a sponge with tiny holes that are linked by little tunnels covered in blood vessels. The air fills these holes then the oxygen mixes in with the blood.)

This means that when we exercise we have to breathe more air in and the heart has to pump the blood carrying the oxygen faster. This is why we breathe harder and feel 'out of breath' and our heart beats faster i.e. our heart rate increases; there are more heart beats per minute.

Why do we get all hot and red when we exercise? This is because the muscles help the liver work. The liver acts like the central heating system for the body. When the muscles work harder, so does the liver and we get hotter – this means that more heat is carried (by the blood) all around the body. Sometimes we work so hard that we get too hot and the body needs to lose heat (from the blood). It does this by losing heat to the air outside the body. The blood deep inside the body can't lose its heat to the air very easily because it is too far away from it. This means that more blood (carrying the heat) is sent to the tiny blood vessels near the skin i.e. closer to the air outside the body so it can lose its heat more easily. This is why we look red because of the extra blood near the surface of the skin. (If we were to get too cold the body would shut down the blood vessels near the surface of the skin so no heat could escape from the blood there. This makes the skin pale or blue.)

❑ Explain 'in your own words' what happens to our body when we exercise.

Name _____

No problem

I am not de problem
But I bare de brunt
Of silly playground taunts
An racist stunts,
I am not de problem
I am a born academic
But dey got me on de run
Now I am branded athletic,
I am not de problem
If yu give I a chance
I can teach you of Timbuktu
I can do more dan dance,
I am not de problem
I greet yu wid a smile
Yu put me in a pigeon hole
But I am versatile.

These conditions may affect me
As I get older,
An I am positively sure
I hav no chips on me shoulders,
Black is not de problem
Mother country get it right,
An juss fe de record,
Sum of me best friends are white.

Benjamin Zephaniah

1. Summarise in your own words what the writer is saying about his relationship with the people at his school, his attitude and theirs.

2. Do you like this poem? Explain your answer.

Name ———————————————

The new teacher

❏ A new teacher walks into the classroom for the first time.
The two passages below describe the first impressions two children in the class have of him. As can be seen they have very different points of view.

Our new teacher strode up and down the classroom glaring at us all. He was a giant... well over six feet tall. He had horrible green glasses. He had cold blue eyes. When you caught his eye you felt like you'd done something wrong. He was wearing a black suit and a white shirt. He looked like he was at a funeral. We all felt it was our funeral!

Our new teacher walked up and down the classroom looking at us all. He was reassuringly tall. He had bright green glasses. He had twinkling blue eyes. When you caught his eye you felt like he was going to be firm but fair. He was wearing a black suit and a white shirt. He looked very smart. We all felt relaxed and confident.

❏ The two passages have the same frame or structure but the different descriptive words and phrases in the passages convey very different points of view. These phrases have been underlined to illustrate this.

1. Underline the six other individual words that convey the different points of view.

❏ The passage below is about a holiday and is written from the point of view of someone who was happy with it.

The owner was very friendly. When I walked in, the hotel was filled with the happy noises of children and adults. She took me upstairs to my room. It was small but cosy. There was a lovely view from the window over a field. The walls were a cheery, bright blue and the curtains were sunshine yellow. My two favourite colours! The bed was a bit hard but I prefer that. There was no television but that was fine. There was a pretty picture over the bed of a young girl in a light pink dress sitting on a bench by a pond on her own.
At dinner time all the guests sat round a large table. The person next to me talked all the time. I liked her. She told lots of jokes. They were really funny. The food was superb as well – tender chicken and crispy chips with lots of fresh vegetables. I knew it was going to be a great holiday!

2. Rewrite the passage from the point of view of someone who didn't like the same holiday, changing descriptive words and phrases appropriately.

Name _____

A bad start

Things were not going well for Miss Rose. She had been ill all of last week but had still done a full week's teaching. She had felt too bad to prepare much at the weekend so she knew she would be struggling this week. First thing this morning she had class 4B. They were not an easy class and Sean always gave her trouble. She loaded all her marking into the car and then turned the key... nothing happened. The car was dead! No!

She arrived at the classroom door five minutes late. She had run for the bus, missed it, and stood in the rain for 20 minutes getting colder and wetter. Class 4B were standing there being really noisy.

She was having a bad start to the day.

"Quiet," she said in a loud voice. They went quiet.

"In we go. Homework on my table before you sit down," she said, opened the door and went in. Just before they came in the door Lenny punched Sean on the back. Miss Rose turned in time to see Sean punch Lenny.

"Right, Sean..first warning. Two more and you're out of here," she shouted.

"But..." Sean began.

"No excuses, Sean. Give me your homework and sit down," said Miss Rose.

"I didn't get a chance to do it. I spent the weekend..." he began.

"I don't want to hear the latest excuse Sean. Second warning. Sit down."

"Lenny and Mike haven't got their homework. Punish them," Sean grumbled under his breath as he went to his place. He wiped a drop of rain from his eye. It was dripping down from his hair. No one cared that he'd spent the weekend looking for his little brother who had run away from home after his mum and dad had another one of their blazing rows.

The lesson was a difficult one for the class to understand and Miss Rose was sorry she hadn't prepared it better. After ten minutes of talking and pointing at the diagrams on the board she asked the class to copy them and explain them in their own words.

Sean had been gazing out of the window. He had tried to listen at first but he hadn't understood what Miss Rose was saying. He had too many other things on his mind.

"I don't know what to do," he said when he realised that the class were all working. The class laughed.

"Third warning Sean. Tina, walk him to the Head," said Miss Rose. She'd had enough!

"No," shouted Sean, "it's not fair!"

❏ From Miss Rose's perspective, or point of view, Sean deserved his punishment. If the Head were to ask Sean for his perspective on what had happened, what would he say? Start with him standing in the line outside the class door and Miss Rose arriving.

Name _____

Macbeth

❏ The text below is based on a classic play written by William Shakespeare, who lived a long time ago. It is about a man called Macbeth and his wife, Lady Macbeth.

Lady Macbeth thought of the king as she had seen him a few moments ago. Asleep. Peaceful. 'Had he not looked like my father as he slept, I would have done it,' she said to herself.

Macbeth appeared on the stairs. He was swaying and his face was the palest white.

"I have done the deed," he whispered. "Did you not hear a noise?"

His wife answered him quickly, "I heard the owl scream and the crickets cry."

She moved towards him. He pulled away and stared at his bloody hands.

"This is a sorry sight," he said.

"A foolish thought to say a sorry sight," she snapped angrily.

He froze suddenly as though he had heard a sound. He pointed a trembling finger, "I thought I heard a voice cry 'Sleep no more, Macbeth has murdered sleep.'"

She seized his arm and her voice was full of scorn now, "Go, get some water and wash this filthy witness from your hand." Then she saw the daggers in his hand.

"Why did you bring these daggers from the place? They must lie there: go carry them," she said in horror.

"I'll go no more!" Macbeth gasped, "I am afraid to think what I have done. Look on it again I dare not."

"Give me the daggers!" She sped up the stairs.

1. Macbeth has killed the king. What evidence is there in the text to suggest that Lady Macbeth was in on the plan?

2. How does each of them now feel about it? (Refer to the text and use quotes where appropriate.)

3. The underlined phrases are written in an older form of English than we speak today. Copy them and underneath each one write what you think it means in modern-day English, i.e. how you might say it.

4. Try and find out about the whole story, then discuss with a friend and then the whole class what you think it is about the story that appeals to so many people generation after generation.

Name _____

The chase

❑ Look carefully at the picture below. The arrows show the route that a suspected criminal took through the hotel he was staying at to escape from a police officer. The route is shown by the arrows. The criminal used anything he could to slow the police officer down, knocking things over and throwing things. Write a description of the chase and the eventual arrest, from the point of view of the police officer.

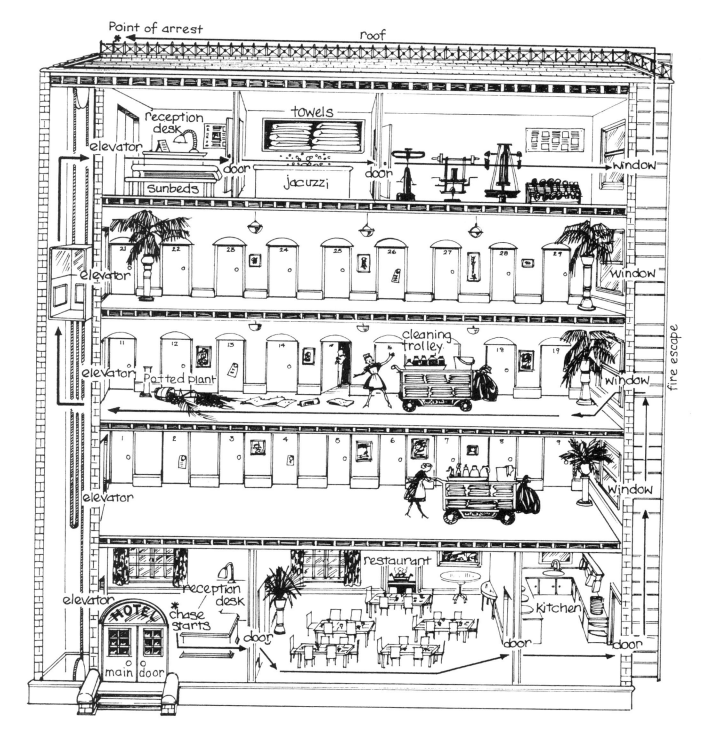

Name _____

Planning is everything

Everything would have worked out beautifully if it hadn't been for the fire alarm! There was the scapegoat – the security guard – who had been suspected of pocketing the odd note from the box office takings. He wouldn't have an alibi and would be watching telly in his room along the corridor from the main office as usual. Who would suspect her? She was well known as a temperamental actress. Everyone knew that she would lock the door to her dressing room and rehearse the next scenes all through the interval. A lot of people had learned the hard way that she wasn't to be disturbed for anything! No one would think anything of the black tracksuit with a hood that she had in the bottom of the wardrobe. No one had seen it before so no one would recognise her from it. No one had seen her bring in the new tape cassette from home that she had spent 20 minutes recording. Everyone knew she liked to listen to music and had a tape player in her room. No one knew she had been a gymnast. She was 50. Who would think she could climb up that drainpipe in the alley behind her dressing room? She had a tool to cut a hole in the window. Into the office, and the box office takings for the last few days were hers. The plastic bag with the tool and the

rolls of money could go in the old drainpipe and she would pick it up later in case the robbery was discovered before the end of the show. It wouldn't be much but she was getting deeper into debt. She was a very accomplished actress who should not have a small part in a small play in a small theatre. She had starred in Broadway shows all her life and was accustomed to a certain lifestyle. The theatre should be paying her so much more. They owed her.

1. What was the actress's exact plan?

2. How long did she plan it would take to commit the crime?

3. Explain from the actress's point of view why she felt her crime was justified.

4. How exactly was she caught?

Name _____

When the teacher went out...

❏ Class 5's teacher, Miss Bradley, was called out of the classroom. Picture 1 shows the classroom when she left. Picture 2 shows the classroom when she returned. The pupils have probably all got different perspectives on what happened, but write from Miss Bradley's perspective what is likely to have happened, and who did what and to whom, while she was out.

Name _____

Dear PE teacher

I think I'd be good at badminton...
If the net wasn't quite so tall!
I think I'd be good at squash...
It's just... I keep running into a wall!
I think I'd be good at weight lifting...
If they weren't such heavy weights
I think I'd be good at ice hockey...
But I've got such slippery skates
I think I'd be good at golf...
If it wasn't so far to the pin
I think I'd be good at baseball...
If the bat wasn't so thin!

I'm going to be a professional sportsperson, Sir
It's what I've always wanted to be
So if I could just have a little encouragement, Sir
Why are you laughing at me?

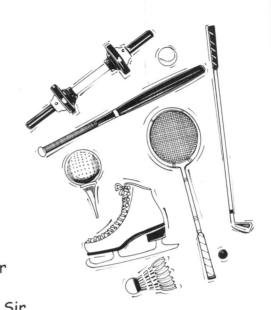

❑ The writer has some novel ideas about how to improve these sports. They are
   listed below. Each idea has ONE word missing. Fill it in.

The badminton net should be _____.
Squash would be better with _____ walls.
Weight lifting would be better with _____ weights.
Ice hockey would be better with _____ slippery skates.
Golf would be better if the pins were _____.
Baseball would be better with a _____ bat.

❑ Complete these extra lines to the poem above in the style of the author:

I think I'd be good at tennis if the racquets weren't quite so _____

I think I'd be good at rock climbing if I wasn't frightened to _____

I think I'd be good at bowling if the bowls would go _____

I think I'd be good at Sumo wrestling if I could just put on some _____

I think I'd be good at football if I could control my _____

I think I'd be good at gymnastics if it didn't make me feel _____

I think I'd be good at fencing but I don't want to be hurt with the _____

I think I'd be good at darts if I could stand closer to the _____

I think I'd be good at swimming if I didn't hate getting _____

.....There's still a couple of sports I haven't tried _____

....

Name _____

A day to remember

Dear Diary,

As you know by now, it's always a day to remember when I go out with my friend Dan! Today we went to watch a cricket match. Dan wanted to get hot dogs and cans of fizzy drink before we went in. I knew we were in trouble when he dropped the cans and I suspected that the huge amounts of tomato sauce he put on his hot dog could cause a problem. I was right on both points. These are the usual sort of problems for Dan, but he surprised even me with his third disaster of the day...

"We'd better open the cans here before we go into the ground. We don't want to spray anyone," I said. Dan nodded and before I could stop him he opened his can and pointed it away from us... and straight at a man who was walking into the cricket ground...

Then came the hot dog incident! All the tomato sauce he'd put on it had lubricated it nicely so that when he bit hard on the end of the bun it shot the sticky hot dog straight out of the other end... and into the lap of a lady in the row in front...

The third disaster came out of the blue... literally! We saw the Kent batsman give the ball an enormous whack. It went up so high I lost it in the sun. I was talking to Dan a few seconds later when the ball bounced right in front of Dan and he caught it! I was so shocked that it had come to Dan and even more so that Dan had caught it that I didn't react quickly enough to prevent the disaster... I blame myself! The Sussex fielder came across to Dan and said, "Well caught son. Pass it here." Dan smiled the broadest smile and took his arm back, aimed and... I saw the rest of this in slow motion as I tried to grab the ball... the ball flew hard to the fielder and hit him right on the nose! OW!

I think that last diary entry surpasses even the ones last month when we went to the park and, among other things, tried to play tennis and the time we went Christmas shopping for presents, including a china teapot!

1. From the diary entry above, describe in a short sentence the kind of problems Dan typically has.

2. What does the writer mean by the phrase, 'out of the blue... literally'?

3. In which season did the author make this entry?

4. Write a diary entry for one of the two events mentioned in the last paragraph. Write it in the style of the person who wrote the above diary.

Name _____

Always there

The room in the pet parlour was very small. Abdul looked down at Jessie in the coffin. She looked peaceful. Like she was asleep. His loyal Jack Russell. He looked carefully at her as if for the first time. She was lying on one side with her eyes closed. Someone had tried to smooth her coat out but it was all in curls going this way and that. It matched her whiskers which were slightly curled at the ends. Her head was a light brown with a white diamond in the middle of her forehead. From the bottom of the diamond a white stripe ran down her nose and then round her mouth. The rest of her coat was white apart from the tip of her tail which was also light brown. He started to smile but the tears came instead.

"She can't be gone Mum!" he sobbed.

"Listen Abdul," said his mother, "What you had with Jessie will always be with you. So Jessie will always be with you!"

"I know," he sobbed. But he wished he hadn't been training so hard lately. Between gymnastics, school, homework and helping in the shop he'd been so busy.

"I can't remember the last time I gave her a bath or took her for a walk!" Abdul sobbed.

"Jessie knew you loved her. You must not worry about that. She knew," his mother reassured him.

Abdul stayed with Jessie for a long time and then gave her one last stroke and closed the coffin lid slowly.

The next day Abdul had both Jessie and Sam on his mind. Jessie had been such a good friend. She was always there no matter what was happening. She was always so pleased to see him when he came home. She was just quietly there at his feet when he was asleep, in the house or at the shop. She didn't ever ask for much. Then there was Sam… He had been his best friend at school. He had always been there for him just like Jessie. He was always listening and offering advice. They used to spend all their free time together. He hardly saw Sam any more. They were in different sets at school and he played more with the other gymnasts in the playground. Then he remembered how the other gymnasts were horrible to him when he didn't do well in team competitions and realised that all they talked about was gymnastics. He didn't want to talk to any of them about Jessie. He grabbed his coat and shoes and ran to Sam's house. Knock. Knock. Knock.

1. What exactly is Abdul feeling guilty about?

2. What do you think Abdul has learned about true friendship?

3. Draw a picture of Jessie.

Name _____

Letter to the editor

I have just returned from the rainforests of South America. This huge forest that is over sixty million years old is nearly the size of Australia! Giant trees reach to the sky and their branches block out almost all the sunlight. It is always hot and wet there. I was lucky enough to meet some of the native people whose families have lived there for thousands of years. Isn't it amazing that two thirds of the world's land animals and plants are in the rainforests? I saw some of the millions of different animals and insects. I will never forget the magnificent sloths, wild boar and parrots. One quarter of all known medicines come from plants and animals found in the rainforest and there are more yet undiscovered. Also, the trees and plants keep our air clean. They absorb the carbon dioxide we exhale and emit oxygen that we inhale. It's an amazing, beautiful place of crucial importance.

So you can understand why I was horrified to learn that rainforests are disappearing at an alarming rate – up to 100 acres every minute (60 football pitches). It's horrifying – millions of animals and the rainforest people are losing their homes and could be gone forever. Medicines as yet undiscovered now never will be and trees and plants that we need will be gone forever.
The trees are being cut and burned and the land ruined and all for money. One of the biggest problems is that there is money to be made in felling timber, building coffee, cocoa and banana plantations, cattle ranching and digging for rich minerals. Pressure groups like Greenpeace do marvellous work and are always taking action to save the rainforests. They also inform people what they shouldn't do. Don't buy stolen bits of the rainforest. Don't buy wooden things made from mahogany, teak, sapele and melanti or exotic animals and plants that have been collected from the rainforest. Some pressure groups even go so far as to block the paths of the bulldozers and chainsaw gangs in the rainforest.

1. Which words, sentences and/or phrases do you think were designed to be most persuasive? Underline them.

2. Imagine that you wrote this letter. You have now been asked to give a talk at a local Greenpeace meeting. You are going to show some slides as well. The information needs to be reorganised. The slides will appear in sets in the order shown below. In note form under the titles Set A, Set B, Set C and Set D summarise what you will talk about as each of these sets of slides is shown. Put any key words in capitals to cue yourself.

   Set A – Slides of the trees and plants and native people in rain and sunshine.

   Set B – Slides of the different animals of the rainforest.

   Set C – Slides of tree-felling and burning.

   Set D – Greenpeace protesters, wooden furniture and parrots and orchids.

Name _____

Polluting the atmosphere

Dear Editor,

I have recently been diagnosed with asthma and was told that a lot more people are suffering from this frightening condition now because of the pollution in the atmosphere. I've done some reading on the subject and what I've learned is horrendous!

Around the Earth we have a layer of gases called the atmosphere. Shockingly the delicate balance of the gases within the atmosphere is being disturbed! We are polluting the atmosphere by putting harmful gases into it. One disaster resulting from this pollution is that the Earth's climate will become warmer and warmer. This will mean problems from the polar ice caps melting as sea and ocean levels will rise. People living in low-lying coastal areas could be under water unless something is done! A second disaster is acid rain, which damages buildings and makes lakes too acid for the fish. A third problem is an obvious one, and one very close to my heart, in that we breathe the air in the atmosphere so, if we pollute it, it will give us health problems including asthma. A fourth problem is that we are damaging the ozone layer, a layer of gas high up in the atmosphere that protects the earth from the harmful ultraviolet radiation from the Sun. This can cause skin cancer which can be fatal!

One of the biggest problems causing the pollution is vehicle exhaust fumes. Each day millions of cars and other vehicles pour toxic fumes into the atmosphere. I walk everywhere now or use public transport – I've sold my car! A second problem is polluting gases called CFCs in some aerosols and refrigerators. I won't buy them now. A third problem is that fossil fuels like coal are burned to generate electricity and this produces polluting gases. I make sure I switch things off when I'm not using them – I don't want to waste electricity! A fourth problem is that industries produce a lot of toxic gases. I'm writing a letter to the government to persuade them to put money into reducing pollution from industries. A fifth problem is rainforests being destroyed as the plants and trees help to keep the air clean. I'm joining Greenpeace, an organisation that is trying to prevent this.

1. Which words, sentences and phrases in the letter do you think are the most persuasive.

2. Having made notes to summarise this information, use these persuasive words and appropriate illustrations to design a leaflet informing people about the dangers of global warming and how it can be prevented.

Name _____

The Ancient Greeks

❑ Below is an extract from a text on life in Ancient Greece for men and women.

Greek women painted their faces with make-up and used hair dye and perfume.

Rich women stayed at home and supervised their slaves. Most women did their own cooking and cleaning – but not shopping. Typical items of food to be bought were garlic, onions, lettuces, grapes and meat. The Greeks bought goods with coins.

Poor women were the only women allowed to work in the fields, planting and harvesting the crops and digging ditches to carry water from the mountain streams to the crops.

Decisions as to how the states should be run were taken at a general assembly which is similar to our parliamentary system. No women were allowed to attend. Every so often the men would meet in a large hall. A rope dipped in red paint was swung behind those who were slow to enter the assembly. Anyone who did not hurry got paint on his clothes and had to pay a fine.

The Greeks were well known for their dramas, and open-air theatres held up to ten thousand people. No women were allowed to act. Masks were used to show different emotions.

Women could not be soldiers. The soldiers mainly fought other Greek city-states.
Those who could afford it had to buy their own shield, helmet, breastplate (covering for the chest), spear, sword and greaves (shin-guards).

❑ Illustrate each aspect of the Ancient Greeks' lives as detailed in the text above. Give each illustration a title.

Name _____

Deserts

Deserts are places where very little rain falls (less than 25cm of rain per year). They are at places on the earth where it is hard for rainclouds to form and so deserts are very dry. About one third of the Earth's land surface is desert. There are different types of desert. There are 'hot' deserts which are dry, dusty and very hot (up to 50 degrees Celsius) during the day but are actually very cold at night because heat is lost rapidly from the ground. The other group of deserts are in certain areas of the polar regions, including Antarctica and Greenland, which also receive very little rainfall. This group of deserts are known as the 'cold' or 'polar' deserts. We are going to look closely now at 'hot' deserts.

Strong winds are common in these deserts, as there are few plants to slow them down (very few plants can survive on such little water). The wind races over the ground whipping up clouds of sand and dust. Sometimes you can't see and have breathing difficulties.

The desert can play tricks on your eyes. You may be fooled into thinking you can see water on the horizon but this is actually a mirage, a picture created by a layer of cold air trapping a layer of hot air next to the ground. This bends the light coming from the cold air and makes it appear like water.

Some of the 'hot' deserts are sandy. Others may be stony, salty or covered in volcanic rock. In the sandy deserts the wind blows the sand across the ground piling it up into giant dunes with wave-like furrows and ridges. The largest dunes are in the Sahara desert and are some 200 metres tall and 900 metres across. In the desert where underground water comes to the surface a rare fertile patch is created. It is called an oasis. There will be a pool of water and there are likely to be palm trees and tall grasses around it. Many desert animals can't survive the heat of the day and only come out at night. During the day though you may see a viper, which uses a sidewinding movement to cross the sand so that its body only touches the sand for a few seconds and doesn't get too hot. You may also see a camel. They are perfectly suited to desert life because their bodies can go for days without water and for weeks without food because of the fat stored in their humps.

❑ Imagine what it would be like for you to be taken, by a guide, for the first time on a camel ride in a sandy desert. Make notes on the relevant information from above first. Key words are all that are needed. Then use them to write a letter to a friend of yours to tell them all about the amazing experience. Use lots of adjectives (descriptive words) for both your feelings and the scene around you.

Name _____

Hunting

Hunting is the sport in which animals (usually foxes and stags, but also sometimes hares) are chased and if caught, killed by packs of dogs.

A debate was held in a secondary school. The motion was 'Hunting is a barbaric sport which should be banned'. Below is a summary of what was said.

Supporters of the motion said first that it was horrific to think of the foxes, stags and hares being torn apart by a pack of dogs and that although foxes were pests and their numbers have to be kept down they could be shot instead. They also pointed out that stags and hares were not pests and that in fact the hare is an endangered species in Britain and needs to be protected. The opponents of the motion argued that since it was necessary to kill the foxes because they were pests, what did it matter how they died?

The opponents of the motion then said that hunting helps to bring money and jobs into the area, for instance people are employed to breed and look after the horses and dogs. As well as this economic importance they pointed out that hunting helps to conserve the land i.e. keep the land in good condition. Supporters of the motion argued against this saying that money, jobs and conservation could be managed in the countryside without hunting if small industries could be developed.

The next argument made by the opponents of the motion was that hunting has been around for a long, long time and it is part of the lives of people brought up in the countryside.

Supporters of the motion pointed out that in fact there were many country folk who wanted hunting stopped for reasons like the damage caused to their land and crops when the hunt passes through.

❑ Make notes to summarise the arguments for and against hunting from the text above. Then copy the chart below onto a piece of lined paper and complete it using your notes.

<u>Reasons to support hunting</u>   <u>Reasons to oppose hunting</u>

Name _____

Rival proposals

A council meeting was held to consider two proposals (suggestions) for uses for a piece of derelict (unused) land on a housing estate. One proposal was for a skate park, which would be fenced off and would be filled with concrete structures to allow skaters to use it free of charge whenever they wanted. The other proposal was for a leisure centre that would take up the same space.

During the presentations lots of issues were raised and discussed. There was a member of the Wildlife Trust present who objected to both proposals because of the plants, birds and insects that would be disturbed. However, members of the council and residents were concerned that the disused land was becoming a dumping ground. People were leaving their rubbish there and it looked awful and was dangerous for the children who might want to play there. Both proposals involved clearing up the rubbish on the land before building began which pleased the residents.

The council was concerned that it would be spending a lot of money to build a skate park and that they would not get any money back whereas the leisure centre would bring money in. On this subject the point was made that the land was in an area of high crime and that this crime was costing money. The crimes were mainly being carried out by teenagers and these same teenagers might prefer to skate for free and have a place they could call their own and so money would be saved that way. The leisure centre would probably not be as attractive to them. Not everyone would be able to use it whereas the skate park would be free.

A lot of residents were behind the leisure centre proposal because of the jobs it would create and because the leisure centre would offer something to both adults and children, whereas the skate park was really only for younger people.

The residents were very concerned about the noise that would be created by both the leisure centre and the skate park but particularly the skate park because it could be noisy both night and day.

❑ Summarise the debate by listing the advantages and disadvantages of both proposals in note form under the four headings `Advantages of the Skate park Proposal', `Advantages of the Leisure Centre Proposal', `Disadvantages of the Skate park Proposal' and `Disadvantages of the Leisure Centre Proposal'.

Name _____

The three states of matter

❑ Everything in the universe is made up of matter. Matter can exist in three states: solid, liquid and gas. So what are the differences and similarities between these three states?

Some liquid matter feels very wet. What happens when you tip it into a container and put the lid on? The first thing you might notice is that all liquid matter flows easily into the container. Another thing you might notice is that all liquid matter changes it's shape to that of the container. If you tip liquid matter into a cylindrical container it becomes cylindrical. If you tip it into a container the shape of a cuboid the liquid matter becomes that shape too. So liquid matter does not have a defined shape. Does the same amount of liquid matter fill containers of different sizes i.e. capacities? To do this it would have to change its volume i.e. the amount of space it took up. The answer is no. There are no liquids that can change their volume. Liquid matter will always take up the same amount of space.

Gaseous matter can be difficult to see and feel. It has not got a defined shape. If you pour it into a container with a lid all gaseous matter will act the same way. It will flow easily into the container and then all around the container taking it's shape i.e. changing shape and moving all around it to fill it i.e. it changes its volume.

Solid matter has surfaces you can feel. Solid matter does not flow easily when tipped into a container. It doesn't change its shape to that of the container and it does not change the amount of space it takes up i.e. doesn't change its volume.

❑ Make notes from the passage above on the defining characteristics of each of the forms of matter. For example, the defining characteristics of liquid matter are the statements that are true of all liquids and are not true of gaseous and/or solid matter. Once you have copied the chart below onto lined paper, use these notes to help you complete the chart by replacing the question marks.

Defining characteristics of matter	Matter		
	Solid	Liquid	Gas
?	?	?	?
?	?	?	?
?	?	?	?

Name _____

The life cycle of an owl

❑ The paragraphs below tell us about the stages of the life cycle of an owl, but they are not in the order in which each stage happens. Number the paragraphs to indicate the correct order.

About a month after the eggs are laid the young chicks hatch. The baby owls are covered in fluffy down which keeps them warm. It grows thicker and turns pale brown until, about eight weeks after they were hatched, the owls have a proper coat of feathers.

The owls find the safest place they can for the female to lay her eggs. This is typically a barn, a hole in a tall tree or church tower. The female owl doesn't make a proper nest. She can lay several eggs but this takes her some time as she can only lay one every two or three days.

In spring, adult owls look for a mate (an owl to have babies with). After mating the eggs are fertilised and begin to grow inside the female. A hard shell forms around each egg when it is big enough and then it is ready to be laid.

The mother owl incubates the eggs (sits on them to keep them warm). This helps the embryo in each egg to grow quickly into a chick. While the mother owl sits on the eggs the father owl brings food to her.

When they are over one month old the young owls practise flapping their wings to make them stronger and then learn to fly. Their parents still feed them for a while until they learn to hunt for themselves. When the young owls are fully grown they have to leave their home and make a new one somewhere else as there is not enough food around the home for the whole family in winter.

❑ Summarise the most important information from each paragraph into one or two short sentences and illustrate it (the illustrations at the bottom of the page may help you) to show the life cycle of the owl.

Name _____

The Loch Ness monster

There is a very deep lake in Scotland called Loch Ness. Some people believe that a strange and giant monster lives there. It has been described as having a body shape similar to a diplodocus but with four diamond-shaped fins replacing the legs. The long neck and tail are both supposedly about the length of its body.

So does it really exist? Over 1,000 eyewitnesses have reported glimpsing the monster and there have been a few photographs of something that could be a strange creature. However one of the most famous photographs taken in 1934 was later found to be of a model stuck on a toy submarine. Perhaps the others were hoaxes. People often make up stories in order to get attention and the people living around Loch Ness earn money as well as attention if people are interested in finding the monster.

In 1987 a sonar scan was made of Loch Ness. This sonar scan was made by creating sound waves in the water that bounce back off objects in the water giving clues about their size and shape. It showed a giant, unidentified object 73 metres below the lake surface. As well as this, unidentified clicking sounds have been recorded.

1. Do you believe from what you have read that there is a strange and giant monster living in Loch Ness or not? Justify your opinion using the arguments above.

2. Draw the Loch Ness monster using the description above.

Name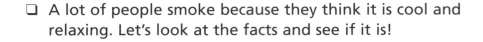

Smoking

❏ A lot of people smoke because they think it is cool and relaxing. Let's look at the facts and see if it is!

When a person smokes a cigarette the smoke is absorbed into the lining of the mouth and lungs. The smoke contains nicotine, which is a very addictive drug. This means that it has a direct effect on the body and mind and makes you 'crave' it (miss it and want it more and more). This is why so many people find it difficult to give up smoking.

Smoke also contains tar and carbon monoxide, which cause health problems for those people who smoke a lot. It affects all parts of the body but the lungs are especially vulnerable. A couple of the problems it causes are breathlessness (the person finds it difficult to breathe) and lung cancer, which can kill.

Smoking also affects the heart. It has to beat faster to get enough oxygen to the cells of the body as the carbon monoxide takes the place of oxygen in the blood and because the arteries (tubes from the heart along which blood travels) become narrower. Among the problems this causes are heart disease and heart attacks, which can kill.

Smokers' teeth become yellow and they often get headaches. Mouth and throat cancers may develop, which can kill.

If a woman who is pregnant smokes it can cause serious harm to the unborn baby. For instance a baby is more likely to be born prematurely before it's lungs are fully developed and so cause it breathing problems.

Scientists have worked out that a person loses about five minutes of their life every time they smoke a cigarette.

❏ Using the information above, design a poster to inform people of the dangers of smoking and persuade them not to. Include the following:

1. Think of a suitable heading – think about how to make it stand out.

2. Think about the pictures or diagrams you will include. Label them.

3. List all the harmful effects of smoking.

4. Include a warning phrase, such as 'Give up smoking before it KILLS you!'